S.I.D
Snake in Disguise

'S.I.D Snake in Disguise'
An original concept by Lou Treleaven
© Lou Treleaven

Illustrated by Louise Forshaw

Published by MAVERICK ARTS PUBLISHING LTD
Studio 3A, City Business Centre, 6 Brighton Road,
Horsham, West Sussex, RH13 5BB
© Maverick Arts Publishing Limited November 2018
+44 (0)1403 256941

A CIP catalogue record for this book is available at the British Library.

ISBN 978-1-84886-385-9

www.maverickbooks.co.uk

Green

This book is rated as: Green Band (Guided Reading)
This story is decodable at Letters and Sounds Phase 5.

S.I.D
Snake in Disguise

by Lou Treleaven

illustrated by
Louise Forshaw

Sid was a snake who found it hard to make friends.

"Hello there," said Sid, popping out of a bush.

"Eek!" screeched Patsy Parrot.

"Howdy," said Sid, slithering out of some grass.

"Get away from me!"

yelled Gemma Giraffe.

"Good morning to you," hissed Sid, sliding out of a hole.

"Aaaah!" cried Zak Zebra.

"No-one wants to be my friend,"

sighed Sid, catching a rat for his lunch.

The rat looked up.

"Maybe you're a bit... you know. Scary?"

Sid found a pool and stared into it.

"Yikes! I can't change how I look.

Or can I?"

But the rat had disappeared.

For the rest of the day Sid
made costumes.

Tomorrow he wouldn't be Sid.

He would be S.I.D: Snake In Disguise!

"Morning," said Sid,
dressed as a giant flower.

"Double eek!"
screeched Patsy Parrot.

"Lovely day," said Sid, dressed as a leafy branch.

"Get away from me now!"
yelled Gemma Giraffe.

"How do you do?" hissed Sid,
dressed as an elephant's trunk.

"Aaaaaaaaaaaaaaaaaaaah!"
cried Zak Zebra.

The elephant wasn't too happy either.

"No one ever wants to be my friend,"
sighed Sid, catching a rat.

"Not again!" sighed the rat.

"Why not try being yourself? And also –
do something nice for a change."

"Like what?" asked Sid.

But the rat had disappeared.

For the rest of the day, Sid tried being a snake. A nice one.

He made a perch for Patsy Parrot.

"Eek, that's comfy," said Patsy.

He made Gemma Giraffe a new scarf for the day.

"Get me!" said Gemma proudly.

And he made an amazing finish line for Zak Zebra's zoomtastic zebra race.

"Aaaaand I've won!" cried Zak happily.

"Thanks Sid," said Zak.

"We like surprises, as long as

they are nice ones."

Quiz

1. What kind of animal is Sid?
a) A giraffe
b) A parrot
c) A snake ✓

2. Why does Sid have trouble making friends?
a) He is too scary ✓
b) He is too funny
c) He is too shy

3. What does S.I.D stand for?
a) Socks In Dirt
b) Snake In Disguise ✓
c) Sniff If Dared

4. Who says Sid should try being himself?

a) A rat ✓

b) A zebra

c) A cat

5. What does Sid make for Gemma?

a) A perch

b) Some lunch

c) A scarf ✓

Turn over for answers

Book Bands for Guided Reading

The Institute of Education book banding system is a scale of colours that reflects the various levels of reading difficulty. The bands are assigned by taking into account the content, the language style, the layout and phonics. Word, phrase and sentence level work is also taken into consideration.

Maverick Early Readers are a bright, attractive range of books covering the pink to white bands. All of these books have been book banded for guided reading to the industry standard and edited by a leading educational consultant.

Pink
Red
Yellow
Blue
Green
Orange
Turquoise
Purple
Gold
White

To view the whole Maverick Readers scheme, visit our website at

www.maverickearlyreaders.com

Or scan the QR code above to view our scheme instantly!

Quiz Answers: 1c, 2a, 3b, 4a, 5c

CODE ACADEMY

and the

Hack Attack!

By Kirsty Holmes

©2019
BookLife Publishing Ltd.
King's Lynn
Norfolk PE30 4LS

All rights reserved.
Printed in Malaysia.

A catalogue record for this
book is available from the
British Library.

ISBN: 978-1-78637-557-5

Written by:
Kirsty Holmes

Edited by:
John Wood

Designed by:
Danielle Rippengill

IMAGE CREDITS

CONTENTS

Words that look like **this** can be found in the glossary on page 24.

REGISTRATION

Another day at Code Academy has begun.
Time for the register! Meet Class 101…

Frankie
Subject: Debugging

Jia
Subject: Hacking

Sophia
Subject: Logic

Ashwin
Subject: Programming

Bailey
Subject: Memory

Simon
Subject: Coding

Today's lesson is all about hacking.
We'll be finding out:

- What is a hacker?

- Is hacking good or bad?

- How to secure your computer.

- What is a strong password?

Ro-Bud

Subject: Playtime!

Code Academy is a school
especially for kids who love
computers... and robots too!
Do I hear the bell...?

MORNING LESSON

The pupils at Code Academy are having a history lesson. Professor Chip is telling them about an **ancient** computer game: Space Invaders.

...and that, class, was the 1980s. Any questions?

Simon wants to know if you could play Space Invaders with your friends **online**. Professor Chip explains that you couldn't because there was no internet for most people in the 1980s.

NO INTERNET?

WHAT?

WHAT?

WHAT?

WHAT?

?

?

?

?

?

LUNCHTIME!

It's lunchtime. The class still can't believe it. No internet? How did people do their shopping or play with their friends?

SEARCH: INTERNET IN THE 1980S

Ro-Bud can **access** the internet. We can look it up!

Ro-Bud tries to access the internet, but something is suddenly wrong. She can't remember how to do it... and she feels all funny...

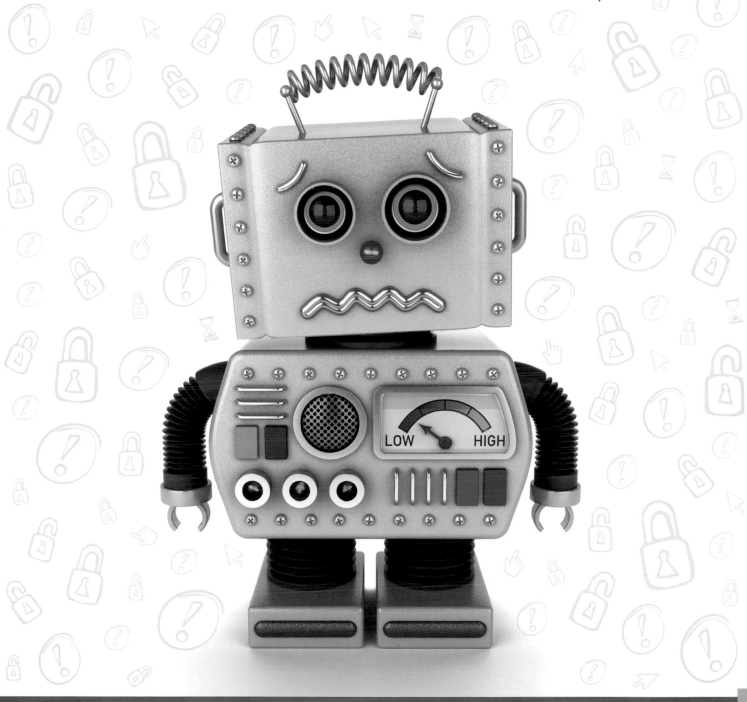

AFTERNOON LESSON

The class take Ro-Bud to Professor Chip. He will know what to do. Professor Chip takes one look at Ro-Bud and grabs a large, heavy book.

TURN OFF...

...THEN BACK ON

CODE

BATTERIES

BUG

VIRUS

POWER

PROGRAM

Hmm. So Ro-Bud is acting strangely...

...and Professor Chip knows why. Ro-Bud has a **<u>computer virus</u>**!

Just like us, computers can get viruses too. They don't shiver or sneeze – but they might start acting strangely. Some viruses can be really serious.

Professor Chip gathers the class around the board.

Somehow, Ro-Bud has got a computer virus. We need to find out what it is, and how she got it in the first place.

INTERNET SECURITY

Professor Chip? I've been looking at Ro-Bud's code. I think she has been hacked. Her passwords have been changed and some **programs** have been deleted.

JIA GETS IN

Hacking a computer means someone is able to access a program or computer that they aren't supposed to, or that is protected by a password. This is very difficult, so hackers are usually very good at programming.

'Hacker' used to mean anyone who was very good at programming.

Hacker

Cracker

If someone used this knowledge to access computers to **sabotage** them, they were called a 'cracker'. But nowadays, we call anyone who sabotages computers a hacker.

Hackers might try to get into a computer to steal information.

THIS COULD INCLUDE:

ID such as a passport or driving licence.

Someone's money and bank details.

Someone's usernames and passwords.

Personal information, e.g. address, phone number.

There are some ways to protect your computer from hackers:

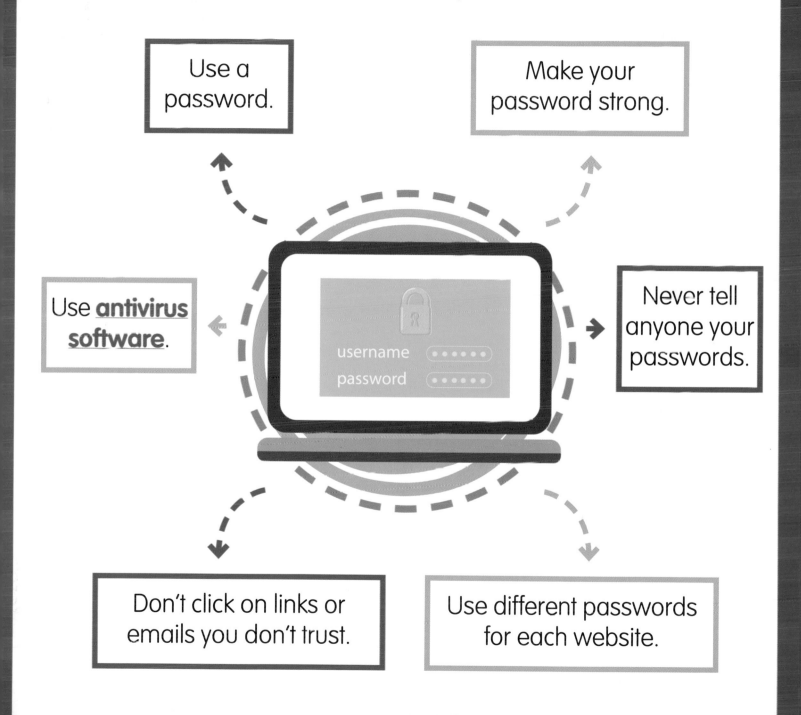

Use a password.

Make your password strong.

Use **antivirus software**.

Never tell anyone your passwords.

username

password

Don't click on links or emails you don't trust.

Use different passwords for each website.

HACK ATTACK!

Professor Chip has removed Ro-Bud's virus, and given her some new antivirus software. She is feeling much better.

And — **REBOOT**!

HIGH

Now, Jia just needs to check that Ro-Bud is properly protected so that she doesn't get any more viruses. Then she will reset Ro-Bud's password.

Antivirus software will protect Ro-Bud like a shield!

It's important to make sure your password is strong and can't be easily guessed – but you will need to remember it too. Here's a handy guide to creating a strong password.

WEAK

Start by choosing something you will remember:

CodeAcademy

Make it longer:

CodeAcademyRules

Mix up the capital and lower-case letters:

CoDeAcaDemyRuLeS

MEDIUM

MEDIUM

Add numbers and special characters:

C00DEAcaDEmyRuLEs!

Maybe spell some things wrong:

C00DEAcaDEmeeRuLEs!

Then add your birthday on the end:

C00DEAcaDEmeeRuLEs!21st

STRONG

If you need to write down your passwords to remember them, keep them away from your computer and hidden away – maybe on a piece of paper between the pages of a book?

ALL SORTED

Now that Ro-Bud's passwords have been changed, she's safe from being hacked for now. But it is important to remember to update Ro-Bud regularly to keep her safe.

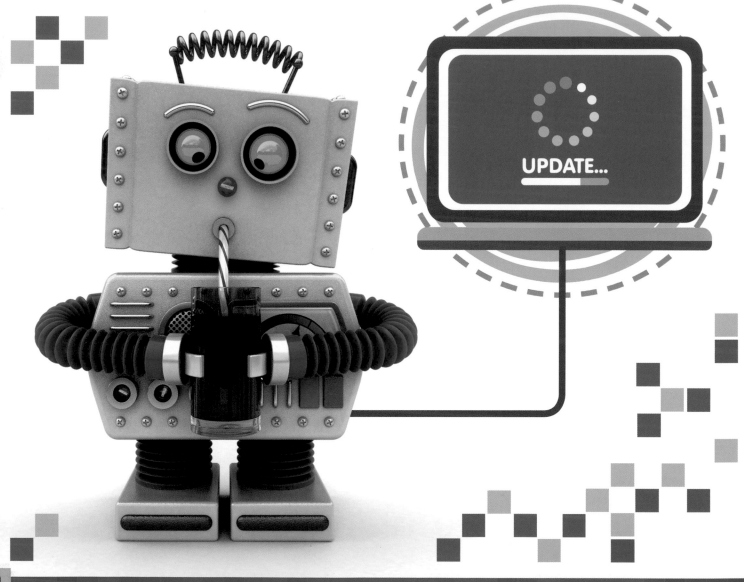

UPDATE...

HOMEWORK

Can you follow the steps on page 20 to create your own really strong password? Here is another way to create a strong password: it's called a base password. Give this a try too – and don't tell anyone!

Pick a word you like:	- - →	YELLOW
Mix it up a bit:	- - →	Y3LL0W
Add the name of the website:	- - →	Y3LL0WScratch
Add a number you like too:	- - →	Y3LL0WScratch21

Whenever you need a new password, use your base password (Y3Ll0W) and add the new website to it.

LOOK IT UP

GLOSSARY:

ACCESS	the ability to enter, use or look at something
ANCIENT	belonging to the very distant past
ANTIVIRUS SOFTWARE	programs that prevent, search for or remove computer viruses
COMPUTER VIRUS	a piece of code that has a bad effect on a computer
ID	short for identification; documents that prove who someone is
ONLINE	something that is on the internet or uses the internet
PROGRAMS	instructions that tell a computer what to do
REBOOT	to restart a computer
SABOTAGE	damage done in secret to stop something from happening or working

INDEX: